# ACCRINGTON STANLEY

*Ground Name*
Fraser Eagle
Stadium/
Crown Ground

*Capacity* 5,057
(2,000 seated)

*Address*
Livingstone Rd,
Accrington,
Lancashire,
BB5 5BX

*Pitch Size* 101.5 x 66 m

*Nickname* The 'Owd Reds/Stanley

*Year Founded* 1968

*Web Site* www.accringtonstanley.co.uk

Accrington were one of the founder
members of the football league.
Following their closure in 1893, a
nearby team, Stanley Villa (named
after their ground in Stanley Street)
renamed themselves Accrington
Stanley.

## I-SPY points: 35

Date: _____

---

*Capacity* 7,100
(2,000 seated)

*Address* High St,
Aldershot,
Hampshire,
GU11 1TW

*Pitch Size* 107 x
69.5 m

*Nickname* The Shots

*Year Founded* 1926 (originally
Aldershot)

*Web Site* www.theshots.co.uk

The current club was formed in 1992
after Aldershot FC closed down
the same year. They began in the
Isthmian League Division 3 and their
local derby that season was against
Camberley Town. Five promotions
and 16 years later, the Shots arrived
in the Football League to reclaim the
place left behind by Aldershot FC.

## I-SPY points: 30

Date: _____

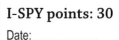

# ARSENAL

*Ground Name* Emirates Stadium

*Capacity* 60,361 (all seated)

*Address* Holloway, Islington, London, N5 1BU

*Pitch Size* 105 x 68 m

*Nickname*
The Gunners

*Year Founded* 1886 (originally Dial Square)

*Web Site* www.arsenal.com

## I-SPY points: 10

Date:

Starting life as Dial Square in Woolwich, south-east London, the club did not move north of the river until 1913. The local Underground station Gillespie Road was re-named after the club in 1932. Arsene Wenger is their longest ever serving manger (since October 1996). They moved to the Emirates Stadium when Highbury closed in 2006, after 93 years.

# FOOTBALL GROUNDS

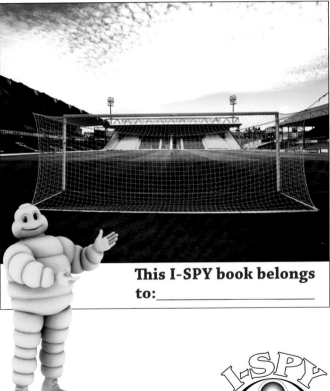

**This I-SPY book belongs to:**_____

# Introduction

Football is an institution in the UK. The first ever national competition played anywhere in the world was the FA Cup, which was first contested in the 1871-72 season, and the first ever league competition was the Football League which began in 1888-89 with 12 founder members. In Scotland the first FA Cup competition was held in 1873-74 and the Scottish League followed in 1890-91.

There are thousands of football clubs all over the country. This book gives you ground information and a small insight into the clubs who make up the Premier League and Football League in England (as well as a few clubs who have recently dropped out of the League), plus the top clubs in Scotland, and the national stadia of England, Scotland and Wales.

In the early days most football grounds would have been mostly open terraces situated close to the pitch, with perhaps one small stand to accommodate seated spectators. This made for an exciting atmosphere when the grounds were full, and this characteristic of British football grounds is still envied all over the world.

More recently health and safety issues have had to be considered, and all clubs have had to upgrade their existing facilities or move to a new purpose-built ground. In fact, of the clubs listed in this book, around one third of them have moved home within the last 30 years.

Note that the pitch sizes are approximate as they can, and are, changed - to suit the home team!

So start with your local club and get clocking up your I-SPY points now!

## How to use your I-SPY book

The book is arranged in alphabetical order of the names to the football clubs. Some grounds are not so easy to spot but even if you Spy them on television you are entitled to half score. You need 1000 points to send off for your I-Spy certificate (see page 64) but that is not too difficult because there are masses of points in every book. As you make each I-Spy, write your score in the box.

## ASTON VILLA

*Ground Name*
Villa Park

*Capacity* 42,788
(all seated)

*Address* Trinity Rd,
Birmingham,
B6 6HE

*Pitch Size* 105 x
68 m

*Nickname* The Villa/The Villans/
The Lions

*Year Founded* 1874

*Web Site* www.avfc.co.uk

Villa were founder members of the
Football League and are one of the
most successful clubs in English
football, with seven League titles,
seven FA Cups, five League Cups and
one European Cup to their name.
Villa Park has hosted 55 FA Cup
semi-finals, more than any other
club ground.

## I-SPY points: 15

Date: _____

## BARNET

*Ground Name*
Underhill
Stadium

*Capacity* 5,500
(all seated)

*Address* Barnet
Lane, Barnet,
EN5 2DN

*Pitch Size* 105 x
68.5 m

*Nickname* The Bees

*Year Founded* 1888

*Web Site* www.barnetfc.com

When Barnet entered the Football
League for the first time in 1991 their
chairman was well-known ticket tout
Stan Flashman and their manager was
the colourful character Barry Fry. The
relationship was fiery to say the least,
and Stan used to sack Barry and then
re-instate him at regular intervals!

## I-SPY points: 25

Date: _____

# BARNSLEY

*Ground Name*
Oakwell

*Capacity* 23,009
(all seated)

*Address* Grove
Street, Barnsley,
S71 1ET

*Pitch Size* 100.5 x
68.5 m

*Nickname* The Tykes/The Reds

*Year Founded* 1887 (originally
Barnsley St. Peter's)

*Web Site* www.barnsleyfc.co.uk

Barnsley were formed by a clergyman,
Tiverton Preedy, in 1887, and have
played more seasons in the second
tier of English football than any other
club – 70 in total. They reached the
top division for the first time ever in
1997 but lasted just the one season in
the Premier League.

# I-SPY points: 20

Date: _____

# BIRMINGHAM CITY

*Ground Name*
St Andrew's

*Capacity* 30,079
(all seated)

*Address* St
Andrews Ground,
Birmingham,
B9 4NH

*Pitch Size* 100 x 66 m

*Nickname* The Blues

*Year Founded* 1875 (originally Small
Heath Alliance)

*Web Site* www.bcfc.com

Way before Manchester United and
Liverpool – Birmingham City were
the first English club in Europe when
they competed in the Inter-Cities
Fairs Cup in 1956. They were also the
first to reach a European final in 1960
when they lost the Fairs Cup 4-1 on
aggregate to Barcelona.

# I-SPY points: 15

Date: _____

# BLACKBURN ROVERS

*Ground Name*
Ewood Park

*Capacity* 31,367
(all seated)

*Address*
Blackburn,
Lancashire,
BB2 4JF

*Pitch Size* 105 x
69 m

*Nickname* Rovers/Blue and Whites/
The Riversiders

*Year Founded* 1875

*Web Site* www.rovers.co.uk

Rovers are one of only three clubs
to be founder members of both the
Football League (1888) and the
Premier League (1992). They are also
one of only four
clubs to win the
Premier League;
this honour came
in 1995 when they
were owned by
local businessman
Jack Walker.

# I-SPY points: 15

Date:

# BLACKPOOL

*Ground Name*
Bloomfield Road

*Capacity* 16,220
(all seated)

*Address*
Seasiders Way,
Blackpool,
Lancashire, FY1 6JJ

*Pitch Size* 102 x 68 m

*Nickname* The Seasiders/
Tangerines/The 'Pool/

*Year Founded* 1887

*Web Site* www.blackpoolfc.co.uk

The Seasiders are easily identifiable as
they are the only team in the league
to wear tangerine shirts. Their finest
hour was the 1953 FA Cup Final when
they recovered from 3-1 down to beat
Bolton 4-3. Stan Mortensen scored a
hat-trick but the match is remembered
for the performance of 38 year-old
winger Stanley Matthews.

# I-SPY points: 20

Date:

## BOLTON WANDERERS

*Ground Name*
Reebok Stadium

*Capacity* 28,723
(all seated)

*Address* Burnden
Way, Horwich,
Bolton, BL6 6JW

*Pitch Size* 100 x
66 m

*Nickname* The Trotters/
The Wanderers/The Whites

*Year Founded* 1874 (originally Christ
Church FC)

*Web Site* www.bwfc.co.uk

Wanderers' greatest ever player was
Nat Lofthouse who died in 2011.
Born in the town, he scored 252 goals
in 455 League appearances (as well as
30 goals for England in 33 matches),
and after his playing career ended
he also served as manager, chief
scout, administrative
manager, executive
manager and
president.

# I-SPY points: 15

<u>Date:</u>

## BOURNEMOUTH (AFC)

*Ground Name*
Seward Stadium

*Capacity* 10,700
(all seated)

*Address* Dean
Court, Kings Park,
Bournemouth,
Dorset, BH7 7AF

*Pitch Size* 105 x
77 m

*Nickname* The Cherries

*Year Founded* 1899 (originally
Boscombe)

*Web Site* www.afcb.co.uk

AFC Bournemouth is just the
simplified trading name for the club
which has been officially registered as
Bournemouth and Boscombe Athletic
since 1923. Their highest ever score
came in 1971 in the FA Cup against
Margate, when Ted MacDougall scored
9 times in an 11-0 win.

# I-SPY points: 20

<u>Date:</u>

# BRADFORD CITY

*Ground Name*
Valley Parade/
Coral Windows
Stadium

*Capacity* 25,136
(all seated)

*Address* Bradford,
West Yorkshire,
BD8 7DY

*Pitch Size* 103 x 64 m

*Nickname* The Bantams/The Paraders/
The Citizens

*Year Founded* 1903

*Web Site* www.bradfordcityfc.co.uk

The Bantams formed in 1903 and
were immediately elected into
Division Two despite never having
played a game before. Valley Parade
has been their only stadium, and
sadly the ground is most famous
for a fire on the last day of the 1984-
85 season when 56 supporters lost
their lives.

## I-SPY points: 20

Date: _____

# BRENTFORD

*Ground Name*
Griffin Park

*Capacity* 12,763
(all seated)

*Address* Braemar
Road, Brentford,
TW8 0NT

*Pitch Size* 100.5 x
67 m

*Nickname* The Bees

*Year Founded* 1889

*Web Site* www.brentfordfc.co.uk

The Bees were a permanent fixture
in Division 1 in their 1930s heyday –
best ever position was 5th in 1935-36.
Their Griffin Park stadium is famous
for being the only ground in English
football with a pub at each corner, one
of which is owned by the club.

## I-SPY points: 25

Date: _____

# BRIGHTON AND HOVE ALBION

*Ground Name*
Falmer Stadium

*Capacity* 22,374
(all seated)

*Address* Village
Way, Falmer,
Brighton,
BN1 9BL

*Pitch Size* 105 x
69 m

*Nickname* The Seagulls/The Albion

*Year Founded* 1901

*Web Site* www.seagulls.co.uk

The Seagulls left their Goldstone
Ground stadium in 1997 and
groundshared at Gillingham for two
seasons, which is 73 miles away!
They then moved to the Withdean
which was an athletics stadium, as
well as serving time as a zoo. The
club moved to
the purpose-built
Falmer Stadium in
2011-12.

# I-SPY points: 25
Date: _____

# BRISTOL CITY

*Ground Name*
Ashton Gate

*Capacity* 21,479
(all seated)

*Address* Ashton
Road, Bristol,
BS3 2EJ

*Pitch Size* 105 x
68.5 m

*Nickname* The Robins/The Reds/
Cider Army

*Year Founded* 1897

*Web Site* www.bcfc.co.uk

Between 1980 and 1982 City became
the first English team to suffer
relegation three seasons in succession,
dropping from the old First Division
to the Fourth. To make matters worse
the club was then declared bankrupt!

# I-SPY points: 20
Date: _____

# BRISTOL ROVERS

*Ground Name*
Memorial Stadium

*Capacity* 12,011
(2,500 seated)

*Address* Filton
Avenue, Horfield,
Bristol, BS7 0BF

*Pitch Size* 101 x
68 m

*Nickname* The Pirates/The Gas

*Year Founded* 1883 (originally Black
Arabs)

*Web Site* www.bristolrovers.co.uk

Rovers supporters are nicknamed the
Gasheads, a derogatory term coined
by Bristol City supporters referring
to the large gasworks which was close
to the Eastville Stadium where they
played for most of their history.

# BURNLEY

*Ground Name*
Turf Moor

*Capacity* 22,546
(all seated)

*Address* Harry Potts
Way, Burnley,
BB10 4BX

*Pitch Size* 105 x
67 m

*Nickname* The Clarets

*Year Founded* 1882

*Web Site* www.burnleyfootballclub.com

Burnley were founder members of the
Football League and are one of just
three teams to have won all top four
divisions. Back in 1910 they changed
their colours from green to claret and
blue to copy Aston Villa, who were the
most successful team at that time.

**I-SPY points: 35**

Date: _____

**I-SPY points: 20**

Date: _____

# BURTON ALBION

*Ground Name*
Pirelli Stadium

*Capacity* 6,912
(2,034 seated)

*Address* Princess
Way, Burton-On-
Trent, DE13 0AR

*Pitch Size* 101 x
66 m

*Nickname* Brewers

*Year Founded* 1950

*Web Site* www.burtonalbionfc.co.uk

The Brewers were formed as recently
as 1950 and reached the Football
League in 2009. When they held
Manchester United to a 0-0 draw at
home in the FA Cup 3rd Round in
2006, Albion were backed in the replay
by 11,000 supporters, the biggest
away contingent ever seen at Old
Trafford.

## I-SPY points: 35

Date: _____

# BURY

*Ground Name*
Gigg Lane

*Capacity* 11,840
(all seated)

*Address* Gigg
Lane, Bury,
Lancashire,
BL9 9HR

*Pitch Size* 102.5 x
67 m

*Nickname* The Shakers

*Year Founded* 1885

*Web Site* www.buryfc.co.uk

Bury beat Derby County 6-0 in the
1903 FA Cup Final at Crystal Palace
and this is still the highest ever
winning margin. Neville Neville, the
father of England internationals
Gary and Phil, is a former director of
the club.

## I-SPY points: 30

Date: _____

# CAMBRIDGE UNITED

*Ground Name*
R Costings Abbey Stadium

*Capacity* 10,847 (4,948 seated)

*Address*
Newmarket Road, Cambridge, CB5 8LN

*Pitch Size* 100.5 x 68 m

*Nickname* United/The U's

*Year Founded* 1912 (originally Abbey United)

*Web Site* www.cambridge-united.co.uk

The U's most successful period was in the early 1990s. In 1990 they became the first team from Division 4 to reach the FA Cup quarter finals, and were promoted through the play-offs. The next year they won the Third Division and reached the FA Cup quarter finals again. Then in 1992 they missed out in the play-offs to join the inaugural Premier League.

# I-SPY points: 25
Date: _____

# CARDIFF CITY

*Ground Name*
Cardiff City Stadium

*Capacity* 26,828 (all seated)

*Address* Leckwith Road, Cardiff, CF11 8AZ

*Pitch Size* 100.5 x 68.5 m

*Nickname* The Bluebirds

*Year Founded* 1899 (originally Riverside)

*Web Site* www.cardiffcityfc.co.uk

Cardiff are the only non-English club to ever win the FA Cup. They beat Arsenal 1-0 in the 1927 final, and the deciding goal was due to a mistake by the Gunners' keeper Dan Lewis, who just happened to be Welsh! In the 2007-08 season, they also managed to reach the FA Cup final, losing 1-0 to Portsmouth.

# I-SPY points: 20
Date: _____

# CARLISLE UNITED

*Ground Name*
Brunton Park

*Capacity* 16,980
(all seated)

*Address* Warwick
Road, Carlisle,
CA1 1LL

*Pitch Size* 102.5 x
67.5 m

*Nickname* The Cumbrians/The Blues

*Year Founded* 1904

*Web Site* www.carlisleunited.co.uk

Three straight wins at the start of
1974-75 saw Carlisle United sitting at
the top of Division 1. However they
went on to finish bottom and that
was their one and only season in the
top flight. At the other extreme, they
were relegated from the League in
2004, only to win their place back the
following season.

## I-SPY points: 25

Date: _____

# CHARLTON ATHLETIC

*Ground Name*
The Valley

*Capacity* 27, 111
(all seated)

*Address* Floyd
Road, Charlton,
SE7 8BL

*Pitch Size* 102.5 x
67 m

*Nickname* The Addicks/The Robins/
The Valiants

*Year Founded* 1905

*Web Site* www.cafc.co.uk

Why are Charlton known as the
Addicks? One theory is that it
comes from the south-east London
pronunciation of "addict" or "Athletic",
but it was more likely given to them by
a local fishmonger who used to serve
the team with haddock and chips.

## I-SPY points: 20

Date: _____

# CHELSEA

*Ground Name*
Stamford Bridge

*Capacity* 41,841
(all seated)

*Address* Fulham
Road, London,
SW6 1HS

*Pitch Size* 103 x
67 m

*Nickname* The Blues

*Year Founded* 1905

*Web Site* www.chelseafc.com

Chelsea have played at Stamford
Bridge since their formation in 1905,
but the stadium was in fact opened
in 1877. For the first 28 years it was
used by the London Athletics Club
for athletics meetings and no football
was played there at all.

## I-SPY points: 15

Date: _____

# CHELTENHAM TOWN

*Ground Name*
Abbey Business
Stadium

*Capacity* 7,066
(3,912 seated)

*Address* Whaddon
Road, Cheltenham,
GL52 5NA

*Pitch Size* 101.5
x 66 m

*Nickname* The Robins

*Year Founded* 1887

*Web Site* www.ctfc.com

The Robins' rise through the
footballing ranks was led by manager
Steve Cotterill. Promoted from
the Southern League in 1997, they
immediately finished runners-up in
the Conference and claimed the FA
Trophy. There was no stopping them
and in 1998-99 they were crowned
Conference champions and joined the
Football League.

## I-SPY points: 30

Date: _____

# CHESTERFIELD

*Ground Name*
B2net Stadium

*Capacity* 10,600
(all seated)

*Address* Sheffield
Road, Whittington
Moor, Chesterfield,
S41 8NZ

*Pitch Size* 103 x
65 m

*Nickname* The Spireites

*Year Founded* 1867

*Web Site* www.chesterfield-fc.co.uk

Like many football clubs Chesterfield
were formed back in 1867 by
members of a cricket club who needed
to amuse themselves during the
winter months. Their nickname is in
honour of the town's most famous
landmark, the crooked spire at the
top of its 14th-century church.

## I-SPY points: 35

Date: _____

# COLCHESTER UNITED

*Ground Name*
Colchester
Community
Stadium

*Capacity* 10,084
(all seated)

*Address* United Way,
Colchester, CO4 5UP

*Pitch Size* 100.5 x
64 m

*Nickname* The U's

*Year Founded* 1937

*Web Site* www.cu-fc.com

Colchester are most famous for
creating one of the biggest shocks
in FA Cup history. As a 4th Division
club they beat the then mighty Leeds
United 3-2 in the 5th Round in 1971
with goals from former England
international Ray Crawford (2) and
David Simmons.

## I-SPY points: 30

Date: _____

# COVENTRY CITY

*Ground Name*
Ricoh Arena

*Capacity* 32,609
(all seated)

*Address* Phoenix
Way, Foleshill,
Coventry, CV6 6GE

*Pitch Size* 105 x
68 m

*Nickname* The Sky Blues

*Year Founded* 1883 (originally Singers)

*Web Site* www.ccfc.co.uk

The club was formed by workers at
Singers cycle factory in 1883. Until
the move to the Ricoh Arena in 2005,
Highfield Road had been their home
for more than a century. In 1981 it
was converted to become the first
English all-seater stadium.

# I-SPY points: 25

Date: _____

# CRAWLEY TOWN

*Ground Name*
Broadfield Stadium

*Capacity* 4,996
(1,150 seated)

*Address* Brighton
Road, Crawley,
RH11 9RX

*Pitch Size* 100.5 x
68.5 m

*Nickname* Red Devils/The Reds

*Year Founded* 1896

*Web Site* www.crawleytownfc.net

In winning the 2010-11 Blue Square
Premier to take their place in the
Football League, Crawley reached a
record points total of 105 and also set
a new milestone by going 30 matches
unbeaten up to the end of the season.

# I-SPY points: 35

Date: _____

# CREWE ALEXANDRA

*Ground Name*
Alexandra Stadium

*Capacity* 10,153
(all seated)

*Address* Gresty Road, Crewe, Cheshire, CW2 6EB

*Pitch Size* 91.5 x 60 m

*Nickname* The Railwaymen/The Alex

*Year Founded* 1877 (originally Crewe)

*Web Site* www.crewealex.net

The club is said to be named after Princess Alexandra of Denmark, the wife of Edward VII. In the mid-1950s Crewe put together a sequence of 56 away matches without a win! They have also finished bottom of the Football League on 8 occasions, more than any other club.

## I-SPY points: 25

Date: _____

# CRYSTAL PALACE

*Ground Name*
Selhurst Park

*Capacity* 26,309
(all seated)

*Address* Selhurst Park, London, SE25 6PU

*Pitch Size* 100.5 x 67.5 m

*Nickname* The Eagles

*Year Founded* 1905

*Web Site* www.cpfc.co.uk

The Eagles reached the FA Cup Final in 1990 for the first and only time, where they met Manchester United. And as this was the first ever 3-3 draw in the final they can claim to have made history. Gary O'Reilly and Ian Wright (2) were the Palace scorers. United won the replay 1-0 five days later.

## I-SPY points: 25

Date: _____

# DAGENHAM AND REDBRIDGE

*Ground Name* Victoria Road

*Capacity* 6,078 (all seated)

*Address* Dagenham, Essex, RM10 7XL

*Pitch Size* 102.5 x 66 m

*Nickname* The Daggers

*Year Founded* 1992

*Web Site* www.daggers.co.uk

In 1979 Leytonstone merged with Ilford. In 1988 Leytonstone-Ilford merged with Walthamstow Avenue to become Redbridge Forest. In 1992 Redbridge Forest merged with Dagenham to give us Dagenham & Redbridge. Simple really!

**I-SPY points: 35**

Date: _____

# DARLINGTON

*Ground Name* The Northern Echo Darlington Arena

*Capacity* 25,500 (restricted to 10,000)

*Address* Neasham Road, Darlington, DL2 1DL

*Pitch Size* 100.5 x 67.5 m

*Nickname* The Quakers/Darlo

*Year Founded* 1883

*Web Site* www.darlington-fc.net

In 1999-2000 Darlington lost an FA Cup tie but still went through to the next round. Manchester United did not take part that season (due to World Club Championship/Intercontinental Cup commitments), leaving an extra place in the 3rd Round. A draw was made from all 20 2nd Round losers and Darlo were chosen. They then lost 2-1 to Aston Villa.

**I-SPY points: 35**

Date: _____

## DERBY COUNTY

*Ground Name* Pride Park Stadium

*Capacity* 33,597 (all seated)

*Address* Pride Park Stadium, Derby, DE24 8XL

*Pitch Size* 105 x 67.5 m

*Nickname* The Rams

*Year Founded* 1884

*Web Site* www.dcfc.co.uk

Derby County won the League in 1972 and 1975 managed by the great Brian Clough and assisted by Peter Taylor. They are the only club to have hosted full England internationals at three home grounds: in 1895 at the Racecourse Ground, in 1911 at the Baseball Ground and finally in 2001 at Pride Park.

## I-SPY points: 20

Date: _____

## DONCASTER ROVERS

*Ground Name* Keepmoat Stadium

*Capacity* 15,231 (all seated)

*Address* Stadium Way, Lakeside, Doncaster, DN4 5JW

*Pitch Size* 113 x 73 m

*Nickname* The Rovers/Donny/ The Vikings

*Year Founded* 1879

*Web Site* www.doncasterroversfc.co.uk

In 1946 Rovers played Stockport County away in a Division 3 (North) cup tie which became the longest ever football match. With the aggregate scores level after 90 minutes, it was decided that play would continue until one team scored. After 203 minutes, with darkness closing in, the game had to be stopped. There are stories of fans going home for their tea, then coming back to watch the end of the game! The replay at Doncaster was won by Rovers 4-0.

## I-SPY points: 25

Date: _____

# EVERTON

*Ground Name* Goodison Park

*Capacity* 40,157 (all seated)

*Address* Goodison Road, Liverpool, L4 4EL

*Pitch Size* 100 x 68 m

*Nickname* The Toffees/The Blues

*Year Founded* 1878 (originally St Domingo's)

*Web Site* www.evertonfc.com

## I-SPY points: 10

Date: _____

The most famous player in the club's history is Dixie Dean. When Everton won the Football League in 1927-28 he scored 60 goals, a feat never achieved before or since. He scored 383 times in 433 appearances for the Toffees, including 37 hat tricks.

A statue of Dixie stands outside the Park End of Goodison Park bearing the inscription "Footballer, Gentleman, Evertonian".

# EXETER CITY

*Ground Name*
St James Park

*Capacity* 8,541
(3,800 seated)

*Address* Stadium
Way, Exeter,
Devon, EX4 6PX

*Pitch Size* 95 x 58 m

*Nickname*
The Grecians

*Year Founded* 1904

*Web Site* www.exetercityfc.co.uk

The Grecians went on a historic tour
of South America in 1914, and it is
believed that the Brazilian national
team played its first ever match
against City. According to different
sources the game ended in a 2-0 win
for Exeter, or it might have been a
3-3 draw...

## I-SPY points: 25
<u>Date:</u>

# FULHAM

*Ground Name*
Craven Cottage

*Capacity* 27,700
(all seated)

*Address* Stevenage
Road, London,
SW6 6HH

*Pitch Size* 100.5 x
68.5 m

*Nickname* The Cottagers/The Whites/
The Lilywhites

*Year Founded* 1879 (originally Fulham
St Andrew's Church Sunday School)

*Web Site* www.fulhamfc.com

Fulham's stadium is an architect's
delight. The Cottage Pavilion was built
in 1905 and can still be seen in one
corner of the ground. Both this and
the Johnny Haynes Stand (named
after their most famous player) are
designated Grade II listed buildings.

## I-SPY points: 15
<u>Date:</u>

# GILLINGHAM

*Ground Name*
Priestfield
Stadium

*Capacity* 11,582
(all seated)

*Address*
Redfern Avenue,
Gillingham,
Kent, ME7 4DD

*Pitch Size* 104 x 69 m

*Nickname* The Gills

*Year Founded* 1893 (originally New
Brompton)

*Web Site*
www.gillinghamfootballclub.com

The Gills are the only Football League
club based in Kent. When Tony
Cascarino was signed from Kent
League team Crockenhill in 1982 the
transfer fee they paid was reportedly
a new set of tracksuits!

# I-SPY points: 25

Date: _____

# GRIMSBY TOWN

*Ground Name*
Blundell Park

*Capacity* 9,546
(all seated)

*Address*
Blundell Park,
Cleethorpes,
DN35 7PY

*Pitch Size* 101 x
68 m

*Nickname* The Mariners

*Year Founded* 1878 (originally Grimsby
Pelham)

*Web Site* www.gtfc.co.uk

Since 1898 Grimsby Town have
played at Blundell Park, which is
actually three miles away in the town
of Cleethorpes, so in many ways, they
are the only team to play their home
matches away! For many years their
mascot was Harry Haddock, in tribute
to the town's fishing industry.

# I-SPY points: 25

Date: _____

# HARTLEPOOL UNITED

*Ground Name*
Victoria Park

*Capacity* 7,856
(4,180 seated)

*Address* Clarence
Road, Hartlepool,
TS24 8BZ

*Pitch Size* 103 x
70.5 m

*Nickname* Pool/Monkey Hangers

*Year Founded* 1908 (originally
Hartlepools United)

*Web Site* www.hartlepoolunited.co.uk

The club's nickname derives from the
Napoleonic Wars when a French ship
was wrecked off the coast of the town.
The only survivor was a monkey who
was brought to trial on suspicion
of being a spy. As he was unable to
answer the questions he was hanged
anyway!

## I-SPY points: 30

Date: _____

# HEREFORD UNITED

*Ground Name*
Edgar Street

*Capacity* 5,075
(2,761 seated)

*Address* Edgar
Street, Hereford,
HR4 9JU

*Pitch Size* 104 x
69.5 m

*Nickname* The Whites/The Bulls

*Year Founded* 1924

*Web Site* www.herefordunited.co.uk

Hereford came to fame in 1972
when as a non-league club they beat
Newcastle United 2-1 in an FA Cup 3rd
Round replay at Edgar Street. Ronnie
Radford's winner is probably the most
famous goal in FA Cup history and the
pitch invasion afterwards has to be
seen to be believed!

## I-SPY points: 30

Date: _____

# HUDDERSFIELD TOWN

*Ground Name*
Galpharm Stadium

*Capacity* 24,500 (all seated)

*Address* Galpharm Stadium, Huddersfield, HD1 6PX

*Pitch Size* 105 x 70 m

*Nickname* The Terriers

*Year Founded* 1908

*Web Site* www.htafc.com

The glory days for the Terriers were way back in the 1920s. In 1926 they became the first club to win three successive League titles, and were then runners-up for the next two seasons. They also won the FA Cup in 1922 and were losing finalists in 1920 and 1928.

## I-SPY points: 25

Date: _____

# HULL CITY

*Ground Name*
KC Stadium

*Capacity* 25,404 (all seated)

*Address* The Circle, Walton St, Hull, HU3 6HU

*Pitch Size* 104 x 71 m

*Nickname* The Tigers

*Year Founded* 1904

*Web Site* www.hullcityafc.net

Until the Tigers were promoted to the Premier League in 2008, Hull was widely held to be the largest city in Europe never to have had a football team in the top division of their national league. Their climb from the bottom division took only 5 years, the third quickest ever.

## I-SPY points: 25

Date: _____

# IPSWICH TOWN

*Ground Name*
Portman Road

*Capacity* 30,311
(all seated)

*Address* Portman
Road, Ipswich,
IP1 2DA

*Pitch Size* 102 x
64 m

*Nickname* The Blues/Town/
The Tractor Boys

*Year Founded* 1878

*Web Site* www.itfc.co.uk

In 1961 Ipswich won the Football
League with Alf Ramsey as manager.
In 1978 they won the FA Cup with
Bobby Robson as manager. Both
moved on to manage the England
team, Ramsey guiding them to the
1966 World Cup
victory and
Robson
taking England
to the World Cup
semi-finals in
1990.

**I-SPY points: 20**

Date: _____

# LEEDS UNITED

*Ground Name*
Elland Road

*Capacity* 37,700
(all seated)

*Address* Elland
Road, Leeds,
LS11 0ES

*Pitch Size* 105 x
68 m

*Nickname* United/The Whites/
The Peacocks

*Year Founded* 1919

*Web Site* www.leedsunited.com

When Don Revie became manager of
Leeds in 1961 he changed their kit to
all white to emulate the mighty Real
Madrid. It seemed to do the trick as
under his stewardship they won the
League three times, were runners-up
5 times, and won the FA Cup for the
only time in their history in 1972.

**I-SPY points: 20**

Date: _____

# LEICESTER CITY

*Ground Name* King Power Stadium

*Capacity* 32,262 (all seated)

*Address* Filbert Way, Leicester, LE2 7FL

*Pitch Size* 102 x 67 m

*Nickname* The Foxes

*Year Founded* 1884 (originally Leicester Fosse)

*Web Site* www.lcfc.co.uk

The club's original name referred to Fosse Road, which was close to their ground. In 1891 they moved to Filbert Street and stayed there until 2002. Leicester are the only team to reach four FA Cup Finals and lose each time.

## I-SPY points: 20

Date: _____

# LEYTON ORIENT

*Ground Name* Matchroom Stadium

*Capacity* 9,271 (all seated)

*Address* Brisbane Road, Leyton, London, E10 5NF

*Pitch Size* 105 x 69.5 m

*Nickname* The O's

*Year Founded* 1881 (originally Eagle Cricket Club)

*Web Site* www.leytonorient.com

For the last match of the 1914-15 season Clapton Orient drew a crowd of over 20,000. They were there to pay tribute to the club because 41 of its players and staff had joined the 17th Battalion Middlesex Regiment to serve in the First World War, the highest number from any football club.

## I-SPY points: 20

Date: _____

# LINCOLN CITY

*Ground Name*
Sincil Bank

*Capacity* 10,120
(all seated)

*Address* Sincil
Bank Stadium,
Lincoln, LN5 8LD

*Pitch Size* 105 x
67 m

*Nickname* The Imps/The Red Imps

*Year Founded* 1884

*Web Site* www.redimps.com

In 1985/86 Lincoln became the first
team to be automatically relegated
from the Football League. They
regained their place at the first
attempt but in all they have been
demoted from the League on four
occasions, more than any other club.

## I-SPY points: 25

Date: _____

# LUTON

*Ground Name*
Kenilworth Road

*Capacity* 10,226
(all seated)

*Address* 1 Maple
Road, Luton,
LU4 8AW

*Pitch Size* 101 x
66 m

*Nickname* The Hatters

*Year Founded* 1885

*Web Site* www.lutontown.co.uk

Luton were the first club in the south
of England to turn professional, in
1891. On 13 April 1936 Joe Payne
scored 10 goals for the Hatters in a
12-0 win against Bristol Rovers; this is
still a record for the Football League.

## I-SPY points: 25

Date: _____

# LIVERPOOL

*Ground Name* Anfield

*Capacity* 45,276 (all seated)

*Address* Anfield Road, Liverpool, L4 0TH

*Pitch Size* 101 x 68 m

*Nickname* The Reds

*Year Founded* 1892

*Web Site* www.liverpoolfc.tv

## I-SPY points: 10

Date: _____

If there had not been a dispute between Everton and their landlord at Anfield, John Houlding, Liverpool FC might never have formed. In 1892 Everton moved to Goodison Park and Mr Houlding founded a new club to play on the Anfield site. The rest is history....

Statue of Bill Shankley, Liverpool's famous manager, outside Anfield.

# MACCLESFIELD TOWN

*Ground Name*
Moss Rose

*Capacity* 6,335
(2,599 seated)

*Address*
London Road,
Macclesfield,
SK11 7SP

*Pitch Size* 105 x
60 m

*Nickname* The Silkmen

*Year Founded* 1874 (originally
Macclesfield)

*Web Site* www.mtfc.co.uk

The Silkmen have spent most of
their life as a non-league club. In
1994-5 they were denied promotion
to the Football League because the
Moss Rose ground did not meet the
requirements. Two years later the
Conference was won again and they
made the step up.

# I-SPY points: 30

Date: _____

# MANCHESTER CITY

*Ground Name*
Etihad Stadium

*Capacity* 47,805
(all seated)

*Address* Sportcity,
Rowsley St,
Manchester,
M11 3FF

*Pitch Size* 105 x
68 m

*Nickname* The Blues/The Citizens/City

*Year Founded* 1880 (originally St.
Mark's (West Gorton))

*Web Site* www.mcfc.co.uk

City's home from 1923 to 2003 was
Maine Road, and initially the club
was hoping to have a stadium with
a capacity of 120,000! Nevertheless
the crowd of 84,569 for an FA Cup tie
with Stoke City in 1934 remains the
highest ever attendance for an English
club ground.

# I-SPY points: 10

Date: _____

# MANCHESTER UNITED

*Ground Name* Old Trafford

*Capacity* 75,957 (all seated)

*Address* Sir Matt Busby Way, Manchester, M16 0RA

*Pitch Size* 115 x 74 m

*Nickname* The Red Devils

*Year Founded* 1878 (originally Newton Heath)

*Web Site* www.manutd.com

When United became the first English winners of the European Cup by beating Benfica 4-1 at Wembley in 1968, their team contained three European Footballers of the Year: Bobby Charlton, Denis Law and George Best, who are immortalised in a statue outside Old Trafford.

## I-SPY points: 10

Date: _____

## MANSFIELD TOWN

*Ground Name*
Field Mill

*Capacity* 7,300

*Address* Quarry
Lane, Mansfield,
Nottinghamshire,
NG18 5DA

*Pitch Size* 104 x
64 m

*Nickname* The Stags/Yellows

*Year Founded* 1897 (originally
Mansfield Wesleyans)

*Web Site* www.mansfieldtown.net

The Stags' greatest period of success
was during the 1920s when they
were a Midland League club, but
six applications to join the Football
League were rejected. In 1931 the
club changed tactics and applied to
the southern section of Division 3.
This did the trick and
they were voted in at
Newport County's
expense.

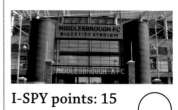

## I-SPY points: 30

Date: _____

## MIDDLESBROUGH

*Ground Name*
Riverside Stadium

*Capacity* 35,100
(all seated)

*Address*
Middlesbrough,
Cleveland, TS3 6RS

*Pitch Size* 105 x
69 m

*Nickname* The Boro/The Smoggies/
The Red Army

*Year Founded* 1876

*Web Site* www.mfc.co.uk

The history of big transfers starts
here! When Middlesbrough signed
Alf Common from Sunderland in
February 1905 they paid a world
record fee of £1,000. In his first match
Alf scored the only goal at Sheffield
United to give Boro their first away
win in nearly two years.

## I-SPY points: 15

Date: _____

## MILLWALL

*Ground Name*
The Den

*Capacity* 20,146
(all seated)

*Address* Zampa
Road, London,
SE16 3LN

*Pitch Size* 96 x
62 m

*Nickname*
The Lions

*Year Founded* 1885 (originally Millwall
Rovers)

*Web Site* www.millwallfc.co.uk

The original Millwall Rovers were
formed by workers from a canning
and preserving factory on the Isle
of Dogs. The Lions can claim to have
hosted the first ever League match
to be played on a Sunday, against
Fulham in 1974.

## I-SPY points: 20

Date: _____

## MILTON KEYNES DONS

*Ground Name*
Stadium mk

*Capacity* 22,000
(all seated)

*Address* Denbigh,
Milton Keynes,
MK1 1ST

*Pitch Size* 105 x
68 m

*Nickname* The Dons

*Year Founded* 2004

*Web Site* www.mkdons.co.uk

MK Dons were formed as a result of
Wimbledon FC's re-location to the
National Hockey Stadium in Milton
Keynes. The club originally claimed
the history of Wimbledon as its own
but now regards itself as an entirely
new club.

## I-SPY points: 35

Date: _____

# MORECAMBE

*Ground Name*
Globe Arena

*Capacity* 6,476
(2,247 seated)

*Address* Christie
Way, Westgate,
Morecambe,
LA4 4TB

*Pitch Size* 105 x
70 m

*Nickname* The Shrimps/The Erics

*Year Founded* 1920

*Web Site* www.morecambefc.com

The club's benefactor in its early years
was businessman J. B. Christie, who
moved to the town when he retired.
He helped arrange the lease of the
original ground, which was re-named
Christie Park in his honour, and his
name lives on to this day at the Globe
Arena which is on Christie Way.

# I-SPY points: 35

Date: _____

 Between 1977-1884
English teams dominated
the European Cup,
winning seven times in eight years!

# NEWCASTLE UNITED

*Ground Name*
Sports Direct
Arena

*Capacity* 52,409
(all seated)

*Address* St. James'
Park, Newcastle-
upon-Tyne,
NE1 4ST

*Pitch Size* 101 x 67 m

*Nickname* The Magpies/The Toon

*Year Founded* 1892

*Web Site* www.nufc.co.uk

It's true to say that the Toon Army
have been starved of success when
you consider that the club's most
successful spell was over a century
ago. Between 1904 and 1911 The
Magpies won the League three times,
the FA Cup once, and were beaten
finalists 4 times.

# I-SPY points: 10

Date: _____

# NORTHAMPTON TOWN

*Ground Name*
Sixfields Stadium

*Capacity* 7,653
(all seated)

*Address*
Sixfields Stadium,
Northampton,
NN5 5QA

*Pitch Size* 106 x
66 m

*Nickname* The Cobblers/Tayn/
Shoe Army

*Year Founded* 1897

*Web Site* www.ntfc.co.uk

The Cobblers have played just one
season in the top flight, back in
1965-66. They had risen from the 4th
Division in just five years, but after
one taste of the big time their fall was
even quicker, and they were back in
the 4th Division again by 1969.

# I-SPY points: 30

Date: _____

# NORWICH CITY

*Ground Name*
Carrow Road

*Capacity* 27,033
(all seated)

*Address* Carrow
Road, Norwich,
NR1 1JE

*Pitch Size* 104 x
67.5 m

*Nickname* The Canaries

*Year Founded* 1902

*Web Site* www.canaries.co.uk

TV cook Delia Smith and her husband
are joint majority shareholders
of the club, and actor/comedian/
author Stephen Fry is also a Director.
The fans' song "On the Ball, City"
is thought to be the world's oldest
football song still in use.

# I-SPY points: 15

Date: _____

# NOTTINGHAM FOREST

*Ground Name*
City Ground

*Capacity* 30,603
(all seated)

*Address*
City Ground,
Nottingham,
NG2 5FJ

*Pitch Size* 105 x
71 m

*Nickname* The Reds/Forest/
The Tricky Trees

*Year Founded* 1865

*Web Site*
www.nottinghamforest.co.uk

When Brian Clough took over as manager in 1975, along with Peter Taylor as his assistant, the club was in Division 2. Promoted in 1977, they then won the League title at the first attempt. More was to follow – Forest beat Malmo 1-0 to take the European Cup in 1979, and they retained it by beating Hamburg (with Kevin Keegan who had signed from Liverpool) 1-0 a year later.

**I-SPY points: 20**

Date: _____

# NOTTS COUNTY

*Ground Name*
Meadow Lane

*Capacity* 20,229
(all seated)

*Address*
Meadow Lane,
Nottingham,
NG2 3HJ

*Pitch Size* 104 x
69 m

*Nickname* The Magpies

*Year Founded* 1862

*Web Site* www.nottscountyfc.co.uk

The Magpies were formed in 1862 and are the oldest existing professional football club in the world. They have been promoted 13 times and relegated 15 times in their history. Did you know that Juventus' black and white striped shirts are based on the Notts County kit?

**I-SPY points: 20**

Date: _____

# OLDHAM ATHLETIC

*Ground Name*
Boundary Park

*Capacity* 10,638
(all seated)

*Address*
Boundary Park,
Oldham,
OL1 2PA

*Pitch Size* 100 x
68 m

*Nickname* The Latics

*Year Founded* 1895 (originally Pine Villa)

*Web Site* www.oldhamathletic.co.uk

Oldham's place in the record books is one they would rather not have! On Boxing Day 1935 they suffered their record defeat, 13-4 at the hands of Tranmere Rovers. This is the game with the most goals ever in Football League history.

## I-SPY points: 20

Date: _____

# OXFORD UNITED

*Ground Name* Kassam Stadium

*Capacity* 12,500
(all seated)

*Address* Grenoble
Road, Oxford,
OX4 4XP

*Pitch Size* 102.5 x
71 m

*Nickname* The U's/
Yellows

*Year Founded* 1893 (originally Headington United)

*Web Site* www.oufc.co.uk

In 1950 Headington United were the first professional club in England to install floodlights. At the time they were playing in the Southern League. The name change to Oxford United in 1960 was intended to give the club a bigger profile, and they were duly elected to the Football League two years later.

## I-SPY points: 20

Date: _____

# PETERBOROUGH UNITED

*Ground Name*
London Road Stadium

*Capacity* 15,314 (all seated)

*Address*
London Road, Peterborough, PE2 8AL

*Pitch Size* 102 x 69 m

*Nickname* The Posh

*Year Founded* 1934

*Web Site* www.theposh.com

In 1921 the manager of Fletton United, forerunners of the current club, said he was looking for "posh players for a posh new team" – and so they became the Posh. Peterborough hold the record for most goals scored in an English season, 134 in Division 4 in 1960-61.

## I-SPY points: 30

Date: _____

# PLYMOUTH ARGYLE

*Ground Name*
Home Park

*Capacity* 18,000 (all seated)

*Address* Plymouth, PL2 3DQ

*Pitch Size* 105 x 72 m

*Nickname*
The Pilgrims/The Greens/Argyle/ The Green Army

*Year Founded* 1886 (originally Argyle)

*Web Site* www.pafc.co.uk

One of the most memorable days in the club's history was in 1973 when they staged a friendly against Brazilian club Santos. Playing for Santos was Pele, possibly the greatest player in the history of the game. This didn't matter to 3rd Division Argyle who pulled off a shock 3-2 win!

## I-SPY points: 25

Date: _____

# PORT VALE

*Ground Name*
Vale Park

*Capacity* 19,052
(all seated)

*Address* Hamil
Road, Burslem,
Stoke-on-Trent,
ST6 1AW

*Pitch Size* 104 x
70.5 m

*Nickname* The Valiants/The Vale

*Year Founded* 1876

*Web Site* www.port-vale.co.uk

The name Port Vale refers not to a
town or city but to a valley of ports on
the Trent & Mersey Canal. The club's
most famous supporter is singer
Robbie Williams, who is now a major
shareholder. Another big fan is darts
legend Phil "The Power" Taylor.

## I-SPY points: 25

Date: _____

# PORTSMOUTH

*Ground Name*
Fratton Park

*Capacity* 21,100
(all seated)

*Address* Frogmore
Road, Portsmouth,
PO4 8RA

*Pitch Size* 105 x
66.5 m

*Nickname* Pompey/Blue Army

*Year Founded* 1898

*Web Site* www.portsmouthfc.co.uk

Pompey won the FA Cup Final in 1939,
beating Wolves 4-1. With World War
II intervening, the next final was in
1946, and so they retained the Cup
for seven years. They won it again in
2008 when Kanu's goal was enough to
defeat Cardiff City.

## I-SPY points: 20

Date: _____

# PRESTON NORTH END

*Ground Name*
Deepdale

*Capacity* 23,408
(all seated)

*Address* Sir Tom
Finney Way,
Preston, PR1 6RU

*Pitch Size* 100.5 x
70.5 m

*Nickname* The Lilywhites/North End/
The Whites

*Year Founded* 1880

*Web Site* www.pnefc.net

Preston were the first champions of
the Football League in 1888-89, and
they also won the FA Cup the same
year to complete the "Double". Their
greatest ever player was Sir Tom
Finney who scored 187 goals between
1946 and 1960 and has a stand at
Deepdale named after him.

## I-SPY points: 20

Date: _____

# QUEENS PARK RANGERS

*Ground Name*
Loftus Road

*Capacity* 18,360
(all seated)

*Address* South
Africa Road,
London, W12 7PA

*Pitch Size* 102.5 x
66 m

*Nickname* QPR/Rangers/The Hoops

*Year Founded* 1882

*Web Site* www.qpr.co.uk

QPR hold the record for the most
home grounds in the history of the
Football League – 14! Their one major
honour came in 1967 when as a 3rd
Division club they won the League
Cup against West Bromwich Albion,
coming back from 2-0 down in the last
half hour to win 3-2.

## I-SPY points: 15

Date: _____

# READING

*Ground Name* Madejski Stadium

*Capacity* 24,161 (all seated)

*Address* Bennett Road, Reading, RG2 0FL

*Pitch Size* 105 x 68 m

*Nickname* The Royals

*Year Founded* 1871

*Web Site* www.readingfc.co.uk

Reading were originally nicknamed the Biscuitmen after one of the main trades in the town, Huntley & Palmers biscuits, but changed to the Royals when the factory closed down in 1970. They reached the top division for the first time in 2006-07 but stayed for just two seasons in the Premier League.

# ROCHDALE

*Ground Name* Spotland Stadium

*Capacity* 10,249 (all seated)

*Address* Sandy Lane, Rochdale, OL11 5DR

*Pitch Size* 104 x 69.5 m

*Nickname* The Dale

*Year Founded* 1907

*Web Site* www.rochdalefc.co.uk

Until winning promotion to League One in 2010, Rochdale had spent 36 years in the lowest tier of the Football League. Outside the top division this is the longest stretch for any team in any division in the history of the League.

**I-SPY points: 20**

Date: _____

**I-SPY points: 30**

Date: _____

# ROTHERHAM UNITED

*Ground Name*
Don Valley Stadium

*Capacity* 25,000 (all seated)

*Address* Worksop Road, Sheffield, S9 3TL

*Pitch Size* 100.5 x 66 m

*Nickname* The Millers

*Year Founded* 1925

*Web Site* www.themillers.co.uk

Rotherham's one and only major final appearance was in 1961, the first season that the League Cup competition was contested. The Millers beat Aston Villa 2-0 at home in the first leg but lost on aggregate after a 3-0 defeat at Villa Park.

# I-SPY points: 30

Date: _____

# SCUNTHORPE UNITED

*Ground Name*
Glanford Park

*Capacity* 9,088 (all seated)

*Address*
Doncaster Road, Scunthorpe, DN15 8TD

*Pitch Size* 101.5 x 66 m

*Nickname* The Iron

*Year Founded* 1899 (originally Scunthorpe and Lindsey United)

*Web Site* www.scunthorpe-united.co.uk

When Scunthorpe moved to Glanford Park in 1988 they were the first club since the 1950s to move to a brand new purpose-built stadium. Two of their best known players, Kevin Keegan and Ray Clemence, went onto fame and international honours in the great Liverpool team of the 1970s.

# I-SPY points: 35

Date: _____

# SHEFFIELD UNITED

*Ground Name* Bramall Lane

*Capacity* 32,702 (all seated)

*Address* Bramall Lane, Sheffield, S2 4SU

*Pitch Size* 102.5 x 66 m

*Nickname* The Blades/Red and White Wizards

*Year Founded* 1889

*Web Site* www.sufc.co.uk

In 1889 an FA Cup Semi-final between Preston and West Bromwich Albion at Bramall Lane attracted a crowd of almost 23,000. The president of the cricket club that owned the ground saw the commercial possibilities and formed the football club six days later!

**I-SPY points: 20**

Date: _____

# SHEFFIELD WEDNESDAY

*Ground Name* Hillsborough Stadium

*Capacity* 39,812 (all seated)

*Address* Hillsborough, Sheffield, S6 1SW

*Pitch Size* 106 x 65 m

*Nickname* The Owls/SWFC/ The Wednesday

*Year Founded* 1867

*Web Site* www.swfc.co.uk

When Wednesday reached the FA Cup Final in 1966 they were drawn away from home in every round. Given the option to wear their home kit at Wembley, they chose to stick with the lucky away strip. But the luck ran out as Everton came from 2-0 down to beat the Owls 3-2.

**I-SPY points: 20**

Date: _____

# SHREWSBURY TOWN

*Ground Name* Greenhouse Meadow/New Meadow

*Capacity* 9,875 (all seated)

*Address* Oteley Road, Shrewsbury, SY2 6ST

*Pitch Size* 110 x 75 m

*Nickname* The Shrews/Salop/ The Blues/Town

*Year Founded* 1886

*Web Site* www.shrewsburytown.com

The Shrews' ground for nearly a century was Gay Meadow, situated on the banks of the River Severn. For many years a local coracle (boat) maker provided an unusual service: he would sit in his coracle during home matches and retrieve any stray footballs which found their way into the river!

**I-SPY points: 30**

<u>Date:</u> _____

# SOUTHAMPTON

*Ground Name* St Mary's Stadium

*Capacity* 32,689 (all seated)

*Address* Britannia Road, Southampton, SO14 5FP

*Pitch Size* 102 x 68 m

*Nickname* The Saints

*Year Founded* 1885 (originally St. Mary's Y.M.A.)

*Web Site* www.saintsfc.co.uk

Centre-half Chris Nicholl made over 600 League appearances for various clubs, but his most memorable was in the colours of Southampton in 1976. Playing against Leicester in a Division 1 match, Chris scored all four goals in a 2-2 draw!

**I-SPY points: 20**

<u>Date:</u> _____

# SOUTHEND UNITED

*Ground Name* Roots Hall

*Capacity* 12,392 (all seated)

*Address* Victoria Ave, Southend-on-Sea, SS2 6NQ

*Pitch Size* 100.5 x 67.5 m

*Nickname* The Shrimpers/ The Seasiders/The Blues

*Year Founded* 1906

*Web Site* www.southendunited.co.uk

The club moved to Roots Hall in 1955, but construction of the stadium was not completed for another 11 years. Roots Hall remained the newest ground in the League right up to 1988, when Scunthorpe moved to Glanford Park.

## I-SPY points: 30

Date:

# STEVENAGE

*Ground Name* The Lamex Stadium

*Capacity* 7,100 (3,142 seated)

*Address* Broadhall Way, Stevenage, SG2 8RH

*Pitch Size* 100.5 x 64 m

*Nickname* The Boro

*Year Founded* 1976

*Web Site* www.stevenagefc.com

Stevenage had their 15 minutes of fame in 1997 when they drew 1-1 at Broadhall Way with Newcastle in the FA Cup 4th Round, then narrowly lost the replay 2-1 at St James's Park. In 2010-11, Stevenage's first season in the Football League, the Magpies visited again for a 3rd Round tie and this time 'The Boro' won 3-1, their first victory against first-tier opposition.

## I-SPY points: 35

Date:

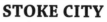 

# STOCKPORT COUNTY

*Ground Name*
Edgeley Park

*Capacity* 10,852
(all seated)

*Address*
Hardcastle Road,
Stockport,
SK3 9DD

*Pitch Size* 101.5 x
65 m

*Nickname* The Hatters/County

*Year Founded* 1883 (originally Heaton
Norris Rovers)

*Web Site* www.stockportcounty.com

In 2011, County dropped into the
Football Conference after 106
years continuous membership of the
League. They hold the joint record
(with Newcastle) for the highest ever
win in a League match – 13-0 against
Halifax Town in 1934.

# I-SPY points: 30

Date: _____

# STOKE CITY

*Ground Name*
Britannia Stadium

*Capacity* 27,740
(all seated)

*Address* Stanley
Matthews Way,
Stoke-on-Trent,
ST4 4EG

*Pitch Size* 100 x
64 m

*Nickname* The Potters

*Year Founded* 1863 (originally Stoke
Ramblers)

*Web Site* www.stokecityfc.com

Stoke's most famous son, Sir Stanley
Matthews was playing for the Potters
in Division 1 when he was 50! Their
first appearance in the FA Cup Final
was not until 2011 when they lost 1-0
to Manchester City, 148 years after
the club was formed.

# I-SPY points: 20

Date: _____

# SUNDERLAND

*Ground Name*
Stadium of Light

*Capacity* 49,000
(all seated)

*Address* Stadium of
Light, Sunderland,
SR5 1SU

*Pitch Size* 105 x
68 m

*Nickname* The Black
Cats/The Mackems/The Lads

*Year Founded* 1879 (originally
Sunderland and District Teachers)

*Web Site* www.safc.com

Sunderland's last major honour was
the FA Cup in 1973, when as a 2nd
Division club they upset the odds by
beating Leeds United 1-0. Manager
Bob Stokoe's triumphant run onto
the pitch at the end of the match is
commemorated by a statue outside
the Stadium of Light.

## I-SPY points: 20

Date:

# SWANSEA CITY

*Ground Name*
Liberty Stadium

*Capacity* 20,532
(all seated)

*Address* Morfa,
Swansea, SA1 2FA

*Pitch Size* 105 x
68 m

*Nickname*
The Swans/The Jacks

*Year Founded* 1912 (originally Swansea
Town)

*Web Site* www.swanseacity.net

In 2011 the Swans became the first
Welsh club to play in the Premier
League. Their original home ground
– the Vetch Field – was named after
a type of bean that was grown on its
surface at the time.

## I-SPY points: 15

Date:

# SWINDON TOWN

*Ground Name* The County Ground

*Capacity* 14,700 (all seated)

*Address* County Road, Swindon, SN1 2ED

*Pitch Size* 91.5 x 64 m

*Nickname* The Robins/Town

*Year Founded* 1879

*Web Site* www.swindontownfc.co.uk

Like QPR, Swindon's one major honour came in the League Cup as a Third Division club. Two extra time goals from Don Rogers saw them beat Arsenal 3-1 in the 1969 final. Playing at left-back was John Trollope who made 770 League appearances for the Robins, an all-time record for one club in English football.

# I-SPY points: 20

Date: _____

# TORQUAY UNITED

*Ground Name* Plainmoor

*Capacity* 6,104 (all seated)

*Address* Plainmoor, Torquay, Devon, TQ1 3PS

*Pitch Size* 102.5 x 67.5 m

*Nickname* The Gulls

*Year Founded* 1899

*Web Site* www.torquayunited.com

When the Gulls lost their Football League status in 2007, chaos ensued. Chairman Mike Bateson resigned, manager Colin Lee was sacked, and former manager Leroy Rosenior was re-appointed and then sacked the same day!

# I-SPY points: 30

Date: _____

# TOTTENHAM HOTSPUR

*Ground Name*
White Hart Lane

*Capacity* 36,230
(all seated)

*Address* Bill
Nicholson Way,
748 High Road,
Tottenham,
London, N17 0AP

*Pitch Size* 100 x 67 m

*Nickname* Spurs/Lilywhites

*Year Founded* 1882 (originally
Hotspur)

*Web Site* www.tottenhamhotspur.com

Supporters' folklore has it that Spurs are successful when the year ends in '1'. They won the League in 1951 and 1961, and the FA Cup in 1901, 1921, 1961, 1981 and 1991. The first Cup triumph came when the club was in the Southern League, making Tottenham the only non-league club to win the FA Cup since the Football League was formed.

## I-SPY points: 10

Date: _____

# TRANMERE ROVERS

*Ground Name*
Prenton Park

*Capacity* 16,567
(all seated)

*Address* Prenton
Road West,
Birkenhead,
CH42 9PY

*Pitch Size* 102 x
65 m

*Nickname* Rovers/Super Whites

*Year Founded* 1884 (originally
Belmont)

*Web Site* www.tranmererovers.co.uk

Rovers live in the shadow of the Merseyside giants, and for a time they played their home league matches on Friday evenings in an attempt to improve attendances. Their only major final appearance came in 2000 when they reached the League Cup final but were beaten 2-1 by Leicester City.

## I-SPY points: 20

Date: _____

# WALSALL

*Ground Name*
Banks' Stadium/
Bescot Stadium

*Capacity* 11,300
(all seated)

*Address* Bescot
Crescent,
Walsall, WS1 4SA

*Pitch Size* 100.5
x 66.5 m

*Nickname* The Saddlers

*Year Founded* 1888 (originally Walsall
Town Swifts)

*Web Site* www.saddlers.co.uk

In 1933 Walsall beat Arsenal 2-0
in the FA Cup at Fellows Park with
goals from Gilbert Allsopp and Wally
Sheppard. This is still regarded as one
of the biggest upsets in Cup history
as Arsenal were about to claim three
straight League titles whereas Walsall
were in Division 3 (North).

# I-SPY points: 25

<u>Date:</u>

# WATFORD

*Ground Name*
Vicarage Road

*Capacity* 17,477
(all seated)

*Address* Vicarage
Road, Watford,
WD18 0ER

*Pitch Size* 105 x
68.5 m

*Nickname* The Hornets/
The Golden Boys/Yellow Army/
The Horns/The 'Orns

*Year Founded* 1881

*Web Site* www.watfordfc.com

Watford's original nickname was the
Brewers, in reference to the Benskins
Brewery which owned Vicarage
Road. They were then known as the
Blues until 1959, when a change of
colours to gold and black and a vote
by the supporters club meant that the
Hornets was adopted.

# I-SPY points: 20

<u>Date:</u>

# WEST BROMWICH ALBION

*Ground Name* The Hawthorns

*Capacity* 26,484 (all seated)

*Address* Halfords Lane, West Bromwich, West Midlands, B71 4LF

*Pitch Size* 105 x 68 m

*Nickname* Albion/The Baggies/WBA/West Brom

*Year Founded* 1878 (originally West Bromwich Strollers)

*Web Site* www.wba.co.uk

Albion have played their home games at the Hawthorns since 1900. At 551 ft (168m) above sea level, the Hawthorns is the highest of all 92 Premier League and Football League grounds. The attendance record is 64,815 for an FA Cup 6th Round tie with Arsenal in 1937. WBA legend Tony Brown holds the club record with 720 appearances between 1963-1981.

## I-SPY points: 15

Date: _____

# WEST HAM UNITED

*Ground Name* Boleyn Ground/Upton Park

*Capacity* 35,303 (all seated)

*Address* Green St, Upton Park, London, E13 9AZ

*Pitch Size* 100.5 x 64 m

*Nickname* The Hammers/The Irons

*Year Founded* 1895 (originally Thames Ironworks)

*Web Site* www.whufc.com

When England beat West Germany 4-2 in the 1966 World Cup final at Wembley, captain Bobby Moore and both goalscorers, Martin Peters and Geoff Hurst – the only man to score a hat-trick in a World Cup final – were all Hammers players.

## I-SPY points: 15

Date: _____

# WIGAN ATHLETIC

*Ground Name*
DW Stadium

*Capacity* 25,138
(all seated)

*Address* Robin
Park, Newtown,
Wigan, WN5 0UZ

*Pitch Size* 105 x
68 m

*Nickname* The Latics

*Year Founded* 1932

*Web Site* www.wiganlatics.co.uk

Wigan Athletic are the youngest club
in the Premier League for season
2011-12, having been formed only
in 1932. The club made headlines
in 1995 when they signed the Three
Amigos – Roberto Martinez, Isidro
Diaz and Jesus Seba. Martinez and
Diaz were the first Spaniards to ever
play in the FA Cup.

**I-SPY points: 20**

<u>Date:</u>_____

# WOLVERHAMPTON WANDERERS

*Ground Name*
Molineux
Stadium

*Capacity* 27,828
(all seated)

*Address*
Waterloo Road,
Wolverhampton,
WV1 4QR

*Pitch Size* 100 x 64 m

*Nickname* Wolves/The Wanderers

*Year Founded* 1877 (originally St.
Luke's)

*Web Site* www.wolves.co.uk

Wolves' most successful period was
in the 1950s when they won the
League three times. Floodlights were
installed at Molineux in 1953 and the
club played a series of promotional
friendlies. One match against Honved
from Hungary was the first ever to be
shown live on the BBC.

**I-SPY points: 15**

<u>Date:</u>_____

# WYCOMBE WANDERERS

*Ground Name*
Adams Park

*Capacity* 10,284

*Address*
Hillbottom Road,
High Wycombe,
HP12 4HJ

*Pitch Size* 105 x
68.5 m

*Nickname* The Chairboys/The Blue

*Year Founded* 1887

*Web Site*
www.wycombewanderers.co.uk

Until 1990 the club played at
Loakes Park which was famous for
its twisting slope – this meant that
when a player took a corner kick
he could not see the diagonally
opposite corner! The club's nickname
recognises the town's long tradition
of furniture making.

**I-SPY points: 30**

Date: _____

# AFC WIMBLEDON

*Ground Name*
The Cherry Red
Records Fans'
Stadium

*Capacity* 5,194
(1,265 seated)

*Address* Jack
Goodchild Way,
422a Kingston
Road, Kingston
Upon Thames, KT1 3TB

*Pitch Size* 100.5 x 68.5 m

*Nickname* The Dons/The Wombles/The
Crazy Gang

*Year Founded* 2002

*Web Site* www.afcwimbledon.co.uk

When the FA allowed Wimbledon
FC to re-locate to Milton Keynes in
2002, supporters opposed to the
move decided to form their own club,
and AFC were born. Playing initially
in the Combined Counties League
their average home attendance was
higher than the exiled Wimbledon
FC! Five promotions in nine seasons
have taken the club to Football League
status in 2011.

**I-SPY points: 30**

Date: _____

## YEOVIL TOWN

*Ground Name*
Huish Park

*Capacity* 9,665
(5,212 seated)

*Address* Lufton
Way, Yeovil,
Somerset,
BA22 8YF

*Pitch Size* 105 x
66 m

*Nickname* The Glovers/Giant Killers

*Year Founded* 1895 (originally Yeovil
Casuals)

*Web Site* www.ytfc.net

Yeovil joined the League in 2003 but
they were famous already for their
sloping pitch at former ground the
Huish, and also for being the most
successful non-league club in the
FA Cup. Their greatest coup was in
1949 when they beat Sunderland and
then faced Manchester United in the
5th Round at Maine Road in front
of more than 81,000 spectators. In
January 2004, prior to their FA 3rd
round cup tie with Liverpool, they
released 'Yeovil True' that reached
#36 in the UK single chart!

# I-SPY points: 30

Date:

## YORK CITY

*Ground Name*
Bootham
Crescent

*Capacity* 7,872
(all seated)

*Address* York,
YO30 7AQ

*Pitch Size* 105 x
67.5 m

*Nickname* The Minstermen/Yorkies

*Year Founded* 1922

*Web Site* www.ycfc.net

The Minstermen spent most of their
League career in the lower divisions
before dropping into the Conference
in 2004. A sponsorship deal with
local employer Nestle meant that for
a number of years the stadium was
re-named Kit Kat Crescent – just what
you need for a half-time break!

# I-SPY points: 30

Date:

## WEMBLEY STADIUM

*Capacity* 90,000 (all seated)

*Address* Wembley, HA9 0WS

*Pitch Size* 150 x 68 m

*Tenants* England National Team

*Year Founded* 2007

*Web Site* www.wembleystadium.com

The original Empire Stadium with its famous Twin Towers was first used for the 1923 FA Cup Final between Bolton and West Ham, when a crowd in excess of 200,000 crammed into the ground and overflowed onto the pitch. The current stadium was opened in 2007 and with a capacity of 90,000 it is the second largest in Europe.

### I-SPY points: 10

Date:

## HAMPDEN PARK

*Capacity* 52,063 (all seated)

*Address* Glasgow, G44 4QG

*Pitch Size* 105 x 68.5 m

*Tenants* Queens' Park F.C.

*Year Founded* 1903

*Web Site* www.hampdenpark.co.uk

There have been three Hampden Parks, and Queen's Park have used all three for their home ground. The current stadium was the biggest in the world when it opened in 1903, and at one stage it had a capacity of over 180,000. The ground is famous for the 'Hampden Roar' created by the crowd to intimidate the opposition when Scotland are playing.

I-SPY points: 15

Date: _____

## MILLENNIUM STADIUM

*Capacity* 74,500 (all seated)

*Address* Cardiff, CF10 1NS

*Pitch Size* 120 x 79 m

*Tenants* Football Association of Wales

*Year Founded* 1999

*Web Site* www.millenniumstadium.com

The stadium, with its retractable roof and a capacity of 74,500, was built to host the 1999 Rugby World Cup and it replaced the National Stadium which stood on the same site alongside the River Taff. It is officially the home of the Wales national rugby team but the football team plays the majority of its matches there also.

I-SPY points: 15

Date: _____

# ABERDEEN

*Ground Name*
Pittodrie
Stadium

*Capacity* 22,199
(all seated)

*Address* Pittodrie
Street, Aberdeen,
AB24 5QH

*Pitch Size* 100 x
66 m

*Nickname* The Dons/The Reds/
The Dandies

*Year Founded* 1903

*Web Site* www.afc.co.uk

Under Alex Ferguson's guidance
Aberdeen won three Scottish titles
and four Scottish Cups during the
1980s. But the greatest achievement
of them all saw the Dons beat Real
Madrid 2-1 to take the European Cup
Winners' Cup in 1983.

## I-SPY points: 20

Date: _____

# CELTIC

*Ground Name*
Celtic Park

*Capacity* 60,832
(all seated)

*Address*
18 Kerrydale St,
Glasgow,
G40 3RE

*Pitch Size* 105 x
68 m

*Nickname* The Bhoys/The Hoops/
The Celts

*Year Founded* 1888

*Web Site* www.celticfc.net

Celtic have won countless honours in
Scottish football but their finest prize
was taken on 25 May 1967, when
they became the first British team
to win the European Cup, beating
Internazionale 2-1 in Lisbon. The
players became known as the Lisbon
Lions and were all born within 30
miles of Celtic Park.

## I-SPY points: 15

Date: _____

# DUNDEE UNITED

*Ground Name*
Tannadice Park

*Capacity* 14,209
(all seated)

*Address*
Tannadice St,
Dundee,
DD3 7JW

*Pitch Size* 101 x
66 m

*Nickname* The Terrors/
The Tangerines/The Arabs

*Year Founded* 1909 (originally Dundee
Hibernian)

*Web Site* www.dundeeunitedfc.co.uk

United have played at Tannadice
Park since their formation in 1909.
The ground is just 160 metres from
Dens Park, the home of their city
rivals Dundee. The two stadia are the
closest of any senior grounds in world
football.

## I-SPY points: 20

<u>Date:</u> _____

# FALKIRK

*Ground Name*
Falkirk Stadium

*Capacity* 9,706
(all seated)

*Address*
Westfield,
Falkirk, FK2 9DX

*Pitch Size* 100.5 x
65.5 m

*Nickname* The Bairns

*Year Founded* 1876

*Web Site* www.falkirk.co.uk

Falkirk is one of two clubs from
the town, the other being East
Stirlingshire. Their previous ground,
Brockville Park, was twice responsible
for them being denied promotion to
the Scottish Premier League for not
meeting the League standards at the
time.

## I-SPY points: 20

<u>Date:</u> _____

## HAMILTON ACADEMICALS

*Ground Name* New Douglas Park

*Capacity* 6,078 (all seated)

*Address* Cadzow Avenue, Hamilton, Lanarkshire, ML3 0FT

*Pitch Size* 105 x 68.5 m

*Nickname* The Accies

*Year Founded* 1874

*Web Site* www.acciesfc.co.uk

The Accies are the only professional club in Britain to have originated from a school team, hence the name. Their best ever player was an Englishman, David Wilson, who scored 246 times for the club before his career was halted by the outbreak of World War II.

## I-SPY points: 20

Date:

## HEART OF MIDLOTHIAN

*Ground Name* Tynecastle Stadium

*Capacity* 17,420 (all seated)

*Address* Gorgie Rd, Edinburgh, EH11 2NL

*Pitch Size* 98 x 67.5 m

*Nickname* The Maroons/The Hearts/The Jam Tarts/Jambos/The Famous

*Year Founded* 1874

*Web Site* www.heartsfc.co.uk

The origin of the club's name is confusing. One theory links it to the Heart of Midlothian jail which was demolished in 1817, but gave its name to a local dance hall. The story then goes that some of the youths who attended the dance hall started to play football together and then founded the club.

## I-SPY points: 20

Date:

# HIBERNIAN

*Ground Name*
Easter Road

*Capacity* 20,421
(all seated)

*Address* 12 Albion
Place, Edinburgh,
EH7 5QG

*Pitch Size* 102.5 x
67.5 m

*Nickname* Hibs/Hibees/The Cabbage

*Year Founded* 1875 (originally
Hibernians)

*Web Site* www.hibs.org.uk

Hibernian were the first British club
to play in Europe after they were
invited to take part in the inaugural
season of the European Cup in 1955.
They overcame Rot-Weiss Essen from
West Germany and Swedish club
Djurgardens IF to reach the semi-
finals, where they were defeated 3-0
on aggregate by Stade Reims from
France.

# I-SPY points: 20

Date: _____

# KILMARNOCK

*Ground Name*
Rugby Park

*Capacity* 18,128
(all seated)

*Address* Rugby
Park, Kilmarnock,
KA1 2DP

*Pitch Size* 102 x
68 m

*Nickname* Killie

*Year Founded* 1869

*Web Site* www.kilmarnockfc.co.uk

Killie took part in the first ever official
match in Scottish football, a 2-0 win
over Renton in the Scottish Cup 1st
Round in 1873. The greatest success
came in 1965, when another 2-0
win at Hearts on the final day of the
season gave them the Scottish League
title for the only time in the club's
history.

# I-SPY points: 20

Date: _____

# MOTHERWELL

*Ground Name* Fir
Park Stadium

*Capacity* 13,742
(all seated)

*Address* Fir Park,
Motherwell,
ML1 2QN

*Pitch Size* 100.5 x
67.5 m

*Nickname* The Well/The Steelmen

*Year Founded* 1886

*Web Site* www.motherwellfc.co.uk

Well's one and only Scottish League
title was claimed in 1931-32. They
scored 119 goals in the process and
Willie McFadyen's contribution of
52 still stands as the record number
of goals for one player in a Scottish
season.

I-SPY points: 20

Date: _____

# RANGERS

*Ground Name*
Ibrox Stadium

*Capacity* 51,082
(all seated)

*Address* 150 Edmiston
Drive, Glasgow,
G51 2XD

*Pitch Size* 105 x 69 m

*Nickname* The Gers/
Teddy Bears/Blues

*Year Founded* 1872

*Web Site* www.rangers.co.uk

Rangers have won the Scottish League
title on 54 occasions, a record for any
team in any league in world football.
The Ibrox stadium hosted the highest
attendance for a league match in
Britain when 118,567 watched the
Rangers-Celtic 'Old Firm' derby on 2
January 1939.

I-SPY points: 15

Date: _____

# ST JOHNSTONE

*Ground Name*
McDiarmid Park

*Capacity* 10,673
(all seated)

*Address* Crieff
Road, Perth,
PH1 2SJ

*Pitch Size* 105 x
68.5 m

*Nickname* The Saints

*Year Founded* 1884

*Web Site* www.stjohnstonefc.co.uk

After winning the 2008-09 Scottish
first division, The Saints were
promoted to the SPL. McDiarmid
Park, opened in 1989 after the move
from Muirton Park, was the first
purpose-built all-seater stadium in
the United Kingdom.

# I-SPY points: 20

Date: _____

# ST MIRREN

*Ground Name*
St. Mirren Park

*Capacity* 8,023
(all seated)

*Address* Greenhill
Road, Paisley,
Renfrewshire,
PA3 1RU

*Pitch Size* 100.5
x 64 m

*Nickname* The Buddies/The Saints

*Year Founded* 1877

*Web Site* www.saintmirren.net

The club is named after the patron
saint of Paisley, St Mirin, who founded
a religious community which became
Paisley Abbey. This all happened
approximately 1,400 years ago! More
recently, the Buddies moved to their
new stadium in 2009 after residing at
Love Street since 1894.

# I-SPY points: 20

Date: _____

# Index

First published by Michelin Maps and Guides 2012 © Michelin, Proprietaires-Editeurs 2012. Cartographic data © Michelin Maps and Guides. Michelin and the Michelin Man are registered Trademarks of Michelin. Designed and produced by Blue Sky Publishing Limited. All rights reserved. No part of this publication may be reproduced, copied or transmitted in any form without the prior consent of the publisher. Print services by FingerPrint International Book production - fingerprint@pandora.be. The publisher gratefully acknowledges the contribution of Des McManus and Tom Hare who wrote the text and for his encyclopaedic knowledge of the subject, and the contribution of the I-Spy Team: Camilla Lovell, Geoff Walls and Ruth Neilson in the production of this title.
The publisher also gratefully acknowledges the co-operation and assistance of the individual grounds, particularly in the supply of images and to the following who supplied pictures for this title: Stewart Walker, Matt Turner, Bill Bearden, Paul Petty, John Marchant and Unitaw Limited. Other images in the public domain and used under a creative commons licence. All logos, images, designs, team strips and image rights are © the copyright holders and are used with kind thanks and permission.
10 9 8 7 6 5 4 3 2 1

# HOW TO GET YOUR I-SPY CERTIFICATE AND BADGE

*Every time you score 1000 points or more in an I-Spy book, you can apply for a certificate*

## Here's what to do, step by step:

### Certificate

- Ask an adult to check your score

- Ask his or her permission to apply for a certificate

- Apply online to www.ispymichelin.com

- Enter your name and address and the completed title

- We will send you back via e mail your certificate for the title

### Badge

- Each I-Spy title has a cut out (page corner) token at the back of the book

- Collect five tokens from different I-Spy titles

- Put Second Class Stamps on two strong envelopes

- Write your own address on one envelope and put a £1 coin inside it (for protection). Fold, but do not seal the envelope, and place it inside the second envelope

- Write the following address on the second envelope, seal it carefully and post to:

I-Spy Books
Michelin Maps and Guides
Hannay House
39 Clarendon Road
Watford
WD17 1JA